# Iron Wheels On Rocky Lanes

**Snippets of memory from a Donegal childhood**

## Hazel Mc Intyre

First published in Ireland in 1994 by
**Moran Publications**
Reprinted 1994
3rd Print, 1995

ISBN 0-9524426-0-4

Typset:            Stuart Clarke
Proofreading:      Colleen Clarke
Cover design:      Robert Clarke
Printed:           Donegal Printing Co.,Letterkenny

For my family
without whose help
and support this would
not have been possible

# Contents

# Foreword

The authoress has given us here a collection of short stories and a number of poems. They deal with interesting and varied vignettes of rural life as found in any rustic community in Ireland.

The ordinary events set on record are infused with the magic touch of the writer. Her sensitivity, her imagination and her empathy give to each episode a deep and wide element of perception. Like a laser beam she enters deeply into the human psyche. She observes; she records.

In her work she goes through the whole gamut of human emotions and feelings. She relates with humour the tale of "The New Suit." The poignancy of the story entitled "Forever Young" touches ones feeling at depth. As she views the ruins of a house whose people took the emigrant ship, one can share her nostalgia for a simple lifestyle that economic necessity harshly teminated.

Hazel is a good storyteller. She carries the reader along with her adding to what might seem a common experience, a special quality. She is truly a close observer of the human situation in all its facets.

There is no sermonising in this book. While she deals with a diversity of characters she sees them all as ordinary, fallible but lovable human beings. She is in full harmony with her background. Here is a book one can recommend whole-heartedly to everyone interested in human nature in all its moods.

Brian Bonner

# Escape

Warm days of summer,
Wandering through dusty lanes,
Strange! I can only remember the warm days,
When I escape back to childhood.

Winter snow crisp and even,
Bright starry nights of frosty magic,
Strange! I can only remember
The clear bright skies of winter,
When I escape back to childhood.

The sound of your voices, the laughter, the
play,
The crimson of a summer dawn,
In the whizzing of a pleasant wind,
Whispering across the hills
I remember you all,
In my escape back to childhood.

# The Return Of A Yankee

The school holidays in summer left us free as the wind to roam far and wide. On warm days we ran to the shore, through the fields and laneways until we reached the golden sandy beach. Hot and sweaty from the exertion, we dived into the cold sea, squealing with excitment as the cold water shocked our warm bodies.

On our route from the beach we usually made two house calls. Sally lived in one with her husband, and she never failed to entertain us delightfully. The two dwellings couldn't have housed two more different characters. Sally had little time for housework, instead she much preferred the great outdoors, tending the animals and poultry. The poultry side of things were her sole responsibility. Her poultry stock was wide and varied, it included hens, geese, ducks, turkeys and guinea hens. The turkeys were sold on the Monday before Christmas, and provided the extra money needed for the

Christmas fare. Although Sally had no family of her own, she had a wonderful rapport with children. She took a special interest in our school work, and was especially good at solving our mathematical problems. She was in her element, when we presented her with a problem we were unable to solve. As mathematics was my weakest subject in school, I often called on her for help.

If Sally had been born in the world of today, she would probably have been a mathematician.

She almost always gave us a detailed account of her household budget.

"The cost of living today is awful, awful," she would complain. "Tea has gone up in price again. My pension goes nowhere. By the time I buy everything needed for the house, and the one and nine pence for Hugh's tobacco, sure I have nothing left out of the ten shillings pension I get," she would tell us, while we nodded at appropriate intervals in sympathy. The concluding part of the cost of living saga usually ended with, "and by the time I put half-a-crown away for my flannel petticoat the money is all gone."

About five hundered yards up the lane, we made our second house call. Anna was a spinster and lived alone. Her cottage was a feast to the eye; roses formed an arch around her front door. Flowers in the front garden grew in profusion permeating the air. The interior was also a joy to behold. Frilly cushion covers on the fireside chairs, snow white lace curtains hung at the window, and the whole effect was one of orderliness and cleanliness. She always made us welcome, and treated us to orange juice and home made buns. But unlike Sally she never confided in us. As a result, we ate and drank, thanked her and went on our way.

One bright sunny morning we made our customary call with Sally. She was seated by the fire as usual, but there was something troubling her. We dutifully admired the young goslings in the wooden box by the fire, even though the clocking hen that was acting foster mother to them, screeched and flapped her wings at us in a frenzy of maternal protection.

We waited patiently to hear about her troubles, for we knew that sooner or later she was bound to tell us; after all we were her confidants.

"I had a letter from my sister Maggie in America. She's coming home to live here for good, and with a husband I have never met," she said, with a stricken face.

"Mind you, I am looking forward to seeing her again in many ways, for it's been forty years since we last set eyes on one another. But

her ways won't be mine. And then there's a
strange man to contend with," she sighed. "I'll
never know what posessed her to marry, at her
time of life. If you are going to marry at all,
when you're young, is the time to do it; not
when your a hairs breadth off sixty." We
listened attentively until she had spoken her
fears before we went on our way again.

Three weeks later, we made ourselves invisible
with the aid of a fuchsia hedge, from where we
watched Maggie's arrival unobserved. She
alighted from a large black car, then a tall grey
haired man got out at her heels. Sally greeted
them warmly enough, with a kiss for her sister
and a firm handshake for the man. The driver
was struggling with three large black trunks,
until Hugh came to the rescue. We watched
until the trunks and passengers disappeared
inside before leaving.
    "It will never be the same in Sally's," John
said sadly as we walked away.
    "Didn't she look a swank though, with that
hat, and all the make-up on her face, not much
like Sally," I commented as we walked on
slowly and a little sadly up the hill.
    It soon became apparent that all was not well
in Sally's domain. Sounds of quarreling were
frequently heard from within. Maggie's fancy
hat was soon replaced with a scarf, and her

crocodile skin handbag with a scrubbing brush.

On a still July evening we could hear raised voices coming from Sally's kitchen.

"You will have to put those dammed birds outside. They have a bad smell," Maggie's angry voice with a Yankee accent, shrilled out through the still air.

"They haven't half as bad a smell as that husband of yours," Sally shouted back.

A few days later Maggie and her spouse left for the town. They bought a house, and lived out their retirement far away from Sally and her birds.

We resumed our usual house calls shortly after the intruders departure. Sally's only comment on the affair was;

"May God protect us all from returned Yanks."

# The Music Room

In the airport lounge I saw him, as I stood
gazing at the passengers as they emerged down
the exit walkway. It had been a year since we
last saw each other.

He still had the same cheeky grin and curling
black mop of hair. "Good to see you again wee
brother," I greeted him.

"Good to see you too sis. It's been a long
time," he grinned as we gave each other a hug.

The following morning I walked out to the
top of the quarry field and breathed in the pure
air. Before me lay the wide expanse of bog
land, peppered with lush green fields, and in the
distance the familiar hills swept down to the
Atlantic. "I'm home," I thought allowing
myself a little squeal of delight.

Then I saw it; the remains of the roof of the
wooden hen house, lying in the quarry below,
where the wind had blown it during that awful
storm in 1957. Memories came flashing back to
me fast and furious at the mere sight of the

black wooden roof.

The new wooden hen house stood at the top of the field, empty; not a hen in sight.

"They have all gone back to the old hen house to roost again," my mother said with a sigh. "Come on you two, give me a hand to get them back." We reluctantly abandoned our play and gathered the sacks as we headed for the old stone hen house. The hens had retired for the night on their roosts in the rafters. Suddenly all hell broke loose, the reluctant hens squawked in protest as we unceremoniously shoved them into the sacks, and transported them once again to the new wooden hen house.

"Don't be so rough with them. You'll stop them laying," she said crossly.

"We're sick of the bloody things. This is the last time I'm doing this," John complained bitterly, his words barely audible above the din of squawking hens.

"If you had rounded them up earlier, like I told you, you wouldn't need to do this," she called back at him. Half an hour later we had finally poked the last reluctant hen down from the rafters and into the sack, and finally to the new hen house.

Another week went past, and still the hens were as reluctant as ever to move into their new abode. If we had failed to round them up and shoo them into the wooden house before twilight, we hightailed it to a safe hiding place in order to avoid the removal process.

Finally much to our relief the reluctant hens won the day, and remained in the old stone henhouse happily roosting in the rafters.

One wet July afternoon we were bored with our confinment to the indoors. After enduring constant chastisements for our noisy behaviour we were reduced to staring out the window. My eyes fastened on the new hen house and a grand idea sprang into my head. "A place of our own to do what we liked in," I thought with delight.

When I made the suggestion to John, he scoffed at the idea. "It would stink, hens dung everywhere," he added wrinkling his nose in disgust. "But we could soon clean it up, scrub it out with disinfectant."

"Count me out. I'm wouldn't play in a smelly hen house for anything," he said sulkily.

"Right then I'll do it myself. But when I've finished it you won't put one foot inside. Do you hear me?" I screeched in annoyance as I stormed off.

"I haven't given up on getting the hens in there yet," my mother said when I broached the subject.

"Please," I pleaded, "we have nowhere to play, and I won't do it any harm, honest."

"Oh, all right. I suppose it will get you out from under my feet. But you will have to get out when I'm ready to put the hens back in," she warned.

The remainder of that day was spent scrubbing and scraping hen dung from the interior. Considering the shortness of the hens enforced residency, they made one hell of a mess.

Finally it was clean, all traces of the hens dung had been removed.


The old shed beside the house held a host of abandoned treasures, old floor mats, a three legged table, and the best find of all; two old fire-side chairs. All in turn were carried or trailed to the wooden henhouse.

However, one minor problem remained; the wooden slatted floor. If a toe or heal got caught between the slats, down you went! A few undignified tumbles taught me the hard way how to tread with care.

With rugs on the floor, the old armchairs in place, and the three legged table propped against a wall, the hens became a thing of the past. But still not satisfied I headed for the house.

"Would you have any old net curtains that

you don't need?'' I asked my mother
cautiously.

"I'll have a look later. But, if you want to
wash the dishes for me I might find time to
look now,'' she added, not missing an
opportunity.

I set to work on the dishes. And half an hour
later the net curtains were hanging on the
window, while I stood admiring the haven I had
created.

Every so often John would poke his head
around the door hoping to be admitted.

"You wouldn't help me do anything, so you
are not coming in,'' I repeated at each attempt,
even though I was becoming bored with my
own company.

"I don't want to go into your old smelly hen
house anyway,'' he said poking his tongue out
at me.

I needed something to do in my new abode, so
I wandered aimlessly around the house
searching. I found a game of ludo and snakes
and ladders, but they needed more than one
player. In the parlour the old church organ sat,
its shiny wood beckoning in the morning sun.
Memory of the music lessons I once had on it
made it less appealing. The droll sound of the
organ music, and the music teacher's ruler
slapping hard on my knuckles made me retreat.

So I abandoned the idea of having organ music. And anyway, I knew that I couldn't hope in my wildest dreams, to get permission to move it.

Suddenly I remembered the gramaphone.

"The very thing!" I thought as I scampered off to find it.

With the gramophone sitting precariously on the three legged stool I put on a record. The strains of Davey Crocket filled the hen house. I sat in one of the arm chairs singing along with the gramophone merrily.

"I know! I'll call it the music room," I decided with sudden inspiration. Just then Davey Crocket slowed down almost to a standstill. I started to rewind the gramophone when I heard the dreaded t-w-a-n-g. The spring had broken, my heart sank as the full implication dawned on me. Then I remembered that Andy Murphy fixed gramophone springs, in fact he could repair just about everything. But how would I carry the heavy gramophone the two miles to his house? There was nothing else for it, I would have to swallow my pride, and get John to help. His help with Neddy the donkey and the cart, would later gain him admission to the music room.

The donkey cart with its iron wheels made a noisy approach into Andy Murphys street. Then we saw him; the village sergeant stood by the turf stack in conversation with Andy's sister.

"Have you a licence for your dog Miss Murphy?" he asked.

"Well now, that's asking me something," she replied, rubbing her chin with a puzzled look, and a twinkle in her eye. "You see he's Andy's old dog, not mine," she added.

"How old is he?"

"Ah, sure he's old enough to get the pension, but they wouldn't give it to him," she replied with a sideways look at the sergeant. We watched him turn his face away from her to hide the broad grin that crinkled his lips.

Clearing his throat, he said, "tell your brother that he would need a licence for the dog, pensioner or not."

"Right you are sergeant, I'll tell him." Maggie assured him. "Licence my foot," she muttered when he was out of earshot. When she saw us, she said cheerily, "Come on in wanes, Andy's in the kitchen."

"I can splice the spring one more time. But it will be shorter, and that will mean more winding of the handle to keep the record spinning." Andy said glancing up at us from above his spectacles, that were perched on the end his nose. We nodded in unison.

Back in the donkey cart I nursed the precious gramophone on my lap as we made our noisy way home.

Old Johnny Taylor's black Ford drove

carefully up behind us. Nudging John on the shoulder, I shouted, "A car, behind us." Looking behind, he yelled back, "Ah, it's only old Johnny. He goes at a snails pace anyway. He can wait 'till we turn off." With that we continued to clatter along in the middle of the lane, with Johnny patiently crawling along behind us.

The newly repaired gramophone proved to be a painful business for the winder. In order to keep the turntable revolving, the handle had to be wound almost continuously, making the music hard earned.

Later during that memorable summer, our older sisters came home for the holidays. And our neighbours from the city came in early August. The music room was a haven for all comers. Inside its hallowed wooden walls the teenagers discussed boyfriends, girlfriends, and the hit parade, while we younger fry wound the gramophone that played songs from another age.

When we tired of continuously winding the gramophone, we created our own music. Our friend Kate from the city, on the comb and tissue paper, John on the tin lid, and myself on the mouth organ.

The summer passed all too quickly, and soon gave way to Autumn and Winter.

A gale force ten from the north west came in February, and took the music room with it. In the morning there was only the bare patch in the field to show that it had ever existed. As we stared at the vacant spot, the hens cackled and the rooster crowed with delight.

# On The Corner

Stand, stare, listen with care on the corner,
Silence only silence.
But wait!
They are still here
Voices, happy young voices,
Now loud and clear, and back on the corner.

From across the time and space
They can still be seen,
And their voice still heard
Back down on the corner.
In spirit it seems they are still
Having fun on the corner.

# The Corner

The familiar voice came to me loud and clear above the noise of the traffic of a busy London street.

"Michael, I can't believe it. Seeing you here," I stammered in disbelief.

"We are both a long way from the corner," he said with his old familiar, cheery lopsided grin.

Over a cup of coffee, we wallowed in unashamed nostalgia.

At the end of our lane was the corner, where four laneways met. This was the meeting place for the young of the neighbourhood. We gathered around the corner in the heel of the evening, to play horse-shoes, sing, dance or skip; all depending on age, and sophistication.

On rainy evenings, we all descended on the inhabitants of the house, that stood beside the corner. Not once can any of us recall being made anything other than welcome. On these occasions, we played cards, sang songs and fought with monotonous regularity. And at the end of the evening, we shared in their supper.

It was Saturday evening in early August, and we were seated on the stone, under the sycamore tree. The familiar sound of the corncrakes filled the still air. Two figures appeared at the top of the brae, on bicyles. We instantly recognised Eddy the barber. But much to our surprise, the young fellow with him was a complete stranger.

"Evening everyone. Anybody need a haircut?" he asked. Eddy stopped at the corner every Saturday evening, on his way to the village, and operated his barber shop by the road side, for anyone in need of a haircut.

"This is Michael," he said, glancing at the young dark haired youth standing holding his bicycle.

"He's on holiday from Edinburgh. Staying with his uncle Pat in Ballycara," he added as he began cutting John's hair, and whistling as he worked.

"Do you want to come with me, or stay with the rest here?" he asked Michael.

"Stay, I suppose," he answered, without showing too much enthusiasm.

When Eddy had gone, he came over and sat with us under the tree.

"Do you like it here?" I ventured.

"It's all right I suppose. But there is nothing much to do," he said sulkily in his strange sounding accent.

"What is there to do in Edinburgh then?"

"You could go to the pictures for one thing. And the bus stop is just five minutes walk from my house, the bus goes all over the city and beyond."

He continued to brag about city life to his captive audience, until we could take no more.

"If the city is so great, what took you here?" someone asked. He just shugged his shoulders again, and was silent.

"Micky Mc Laughlin's cow is stuck in the upper part of the river," an excited wee voice called breathlessly. So off we all trooped in the direction of the men with ropes, crossing the distant field.

On the river bank we stood in a row, and watched as the ropes were secured around the under-belly of the exhausted, and terrified animal.

"Take it easy now. Heave, heave," they called, as bit, by bit, the cow was pulled out unto the safety of the hard ground. The cow sat and rested for a while, before getting up and walking a little shakily back to join the herd. The emergency over, we walked back to the corner, to continue with our game of horseshoes.

The rain finally ceased on Monday evening, and we all made our way down to the corner as usual. As the evening air grew still, the midges swarmed around us, and feasted on our legs, arms and scalp.

"How about going down to Murphy's for some sweets?" someone suggested.

We gathered up our collection of rusty bicycles, including Michaels shiny new, city bicycle, and off we set. Those of us who didn't have a bicycle hitched a lift on a crossbar or parcel carrier.

We rode down the hills at speed, the wind, freeing us from the dreaded midges.

We crowded into Murphy's shop with our pennies, and with much pondering, and great patience from the shopkeeper we chose our sweets.

On the village green we chewed our way through the sweets. Kate and I looked longingly at the younger boys, munching the liquorice, black-jack toffees. Although, they were our favourites, we couldn't risk the black coloured teeth and lips; at least not while Michael, and Kate's heart-throb James were looking admiringly in our direction. Instead, we nibbled our dainty marshmallows, while keeping an envious eye on the black-jacks.

It was almost dark by the time we headed towards home. The younger ones had gone on ahead of us, leaving Kate, Michael, James and myself. We dawdled up the lane until we almost reached the corner. Then we saw the glow from the hurricane lamp, coming down our lane.

"We're in trouble. Looks like they are on the war path," Kate whispered anxiously.

"Quick, we'll hide, in here," Michael whispered in his Edinburgh twang.

We quickly discarded the bicycle, and dived for cover into a little wooded area. We lay in the long grass, hardly daring to breathe. We listened to our mothers' voices, while our hearts thundered loudly in our ears.

"Where on earth could they be until this hour?" my mother's familiar voice echoed through the stillness. When Kate gets back, she will have some explaining to do."

We lay deathly still, and listened as they scolded and complained about their wayward, thoughtless daughters, for what seemed like an eternity.

At last their voices began to fade, as they moved on up the lane.

Jumping hastily to our feet, we bid our companions good night, and ran hell for leather up home through the fields, reaching Kate's house ahead of our angry mothers.

Kate's father sat by the range, with his feet on the fender, reading a book.

"I think there is a search party out for you two," he said with a small grin.

"If they ask, say we have been here for a while," Kate panted.

He glanced at us for a few seconds, before he spoke.

"I'm not going to lie for you. But if they don't ask, I'll say nothing. I hope you have time to get your breath back before they get here," he added with a sideways glance, that failed to hide his amusement.

When they came in the door a few minutes later, we were sitting at the table, with a pack of cards, trying to look as casual as possible.

"We were out looking for you two," Kate's Mother said angrily.

"You must have missed us." Kate said.

"We have been here a good wee while." I fibbed. Her father cleared his throat, as if he were about to speak. But true to his word, he said nothing. Soon they began talking between themselves, and we said a silent 'thank you.'

As we sat looking out at the continuous London traffic, Michael said; "That summer in Donegal was the happiest one of my entire life. I cried like a baby all the way back to Edinburgh,"

He stared straight ahead with a wistful, misty look in his eyes, before he spoke again. "I got an earwig in my right ear that night, when we hid in the damp grass. I thought I would never get the damned thing out. But it was a small price to pay, for the fun at the corner."

# Cleanliness Next To Godliness

Elizabeth is the second eldest of the family. She made herself responsible for keeping the younger members of the brood clean. On bath nights she would descend on us unawares, leaving us no escape route from her clutches.

In a small tin basin, the shampoo powder would have been mixed with warm water, and then our torture would begin. She would scrub us, one at a time from head to toe, while we yelled in useless protest. When the torturous procedure was finished, we each emerged from the water like lobsters, rubbing our stinging eyes, that the dreaded shampoo had seeped into.

During school terms she was our driver, and protector all in one. Because the distance to school was too far to walk, our uncle gave us his pony and trap.

Jackie the pony was a black gelding, with a white star on his head. We were as proud as peacocks arriving at school in the trap, with Jackie stepping smartly into the school yard.

We would all make our way into the school, while big sister unharnessed Jackie and gave him his hay and oats.

Reverend Jones came into school each morning, for morning prayer. But the prayers were almost always delayed until Elizabeth had attended to the pony's needs.

He would march up and down the floor looking at his watch impatiently.

"How much longer is that girl going to be?" he would ask, looking from one of us to the other in some bewilderment while we related the long list of Jackie's morning requirements.

"At long last, you have decided to honour us with your presence," he would say somewhat sarcastically, when she would finally make an appearance.

On one fine September afternoon mother had given us instructions to collect a roll of linoleum from the village shop on our way home. With the aid of the shopkeeper we got the linoleum into the trap, then we all piled in around it, and headed for home.

A short distance from the village, Elizabeth gave Jackie his head as usual. Suddenly he caught sight of the long roll looming above his head. And like all the demons in hell were in pursuit, he bolted down the road at speed. Clinging tightly to the sides of the trap, we hung on for dear life.

Above the noise of the fleeing hooves and clanking wheels, she shouted.

"Throw the damned lino over the ditch, when I say. One, two, three, HEAVE." The roll went over the ditch in haste, and landed in a field. Then with relief we reached the big brae. The upwards pull finally slowed the terrified animal down to a trot, then finally to a walk.

"We'll go back for the lino. And for heavens sake don't go dramatising anything when we get home, or you might end up walking to school tomorrow," she warned the three white, terrified faces, that stared back at her nodding silently.

With a struggle we managed to get the linoleum back into the trap. But this time horizontally across. Then we all held it carefully in position, while big sister kept a tight rein on Jackie.

Many years later, I found myself helping my mother to get the kitchen floor stripped and ready for new floor covering. The rust coloured linoleum that had been hidden under a second layer, brought the memory of Jackie flooding back.

"I'll never forget the day we took this stuff home in the trap," I said.

"I heard all about it from Johnnie Healey.

The poor man could have lost his head.''

"What do you mean?'' I asked a little bewildered.

"Well, he told me he was draining a ditch, in the field when suddenly, this long roll flew past his head. It just missed him by inches,'' she said, shaking her head reprovingly.

# A Feast Of Food And Light

We slowly made our way home from school, feasting on nature's autumn goodies along the lanes in the warm sunshine.

Haws from the hawthorn bushes, blackberries, hazel nuts and wild sloes were devoured as we went. The hedge rows were red with fuchsia. We plucked off the flowers and sucked the sweet juices for dessert.

"I am going to dig the potatoes at the port tomorrow," my father announced at supper time.

"Will you be needing us?" I asked hopefully, as a day of freedom from school loomed invitingly before me.

"Aye, I'll be needing all the help I can get."

With that, I quickly put the school homework to one side to seek a more entertaining pursuit.

Bright and early the following morning we set

off for the port, and the potato harvest.

As the day progressed, and our backs ached with the constant bending, school didn't seem so bad after all.

"I'm hungry. Could you get a couple of crabs. We could light a fire and cook them?" John asked my father.

He shook his head ruefully, but went off in the direction of the rocks where the crabs hung out. Ten minutes later he emerged from behind a rock, holding two large wriggling crabs. When the fire was lit, and the bucket of spring water had reached boiling point, we immersed the poor unfortunate crabs into the bubbling water, while we turned our heads the other way. While the crabs and winkles cooled, we washed the potatoes in the sea and boiled them in the same water. When the feast was prepared, we invited the workers to dine.

But when the feast was over, and our stomachs full, we had no further excuse to avoid the potato gathering.

As dusk fell, we made our weary way home, stopping occasionally to rub our aching backs. When we reached the top of the brae, we saw the big van with, ESB written on the side in large, bold letters.

"The electric is going to be connected," John shouted excitedly, suddenly bolting on ahead, his tiredness forgotten.

I trudged on up the hill slowly, unable to contain my excitement. An electric radio of my very own, was the object of my heart's desire, as I remembered my mother's promise;

"When we get the electricity, I will buy you a radio of your own," she had said, as she praised my housekeeping efforts, on her return from visiting a sick relative.

"My stomach will never be the same again. Not even the dog would risk the bread she made," my father complained.

"But I suppose she did her best, for a ten year old," he added graciously. But, bad stomach or not, I was anticipating the radio with mounting glee.

We all stood watching the ceiling, as the light was switched on. As the bright light lit up the kitchen, we stared in wonder at the sheer magic of it. During the course of the evening, the light switches were in constant use. Where there was darkness; at the flick of a switch we revelled in the instant electric light, that was until the novelty wore off.

On Saturday evening we called in to see Sally, on our way from the village shop as usual. The only light in her kitchen came from her turf fire.

"Have you not switched on your electric light yet," John asked.

"I suppose it's time I lit it," she said with a sigh. In the dim light we watched her get a broom handle from the corner, and aim it in the direction of the switch. The target was missed a few times, before she eventually managed to engage the switch with the broom handle, and the kitchen glowed with light. A long low sigh escaped from her throat, before she spoke.

"You have to be careful with the electric you know," she said, while we stifled a giggle. Then she went over to a shelf, and came back with a can of oil. We watched her fill the oil lamp carefully with the oil, and as she sat down again, she said, "Just in case."

# Horizons

From the hill we watched the snug white
houses,
Under their coating of cockle lime
Making up our world in the growing years-
A world that only stretched as far,
As the last blue line of
Mountains - ever so far away-
To the next horizon, and no further.

From the narrow grey roads
That crossed brown moors-
And bridges that crossed rushing streams.
We were given the roots to grow
And the wings to fly.

# The Contraption.

The hands of the school clock slowly wound their way towards three o'clock. My mind was far away from the history lesson in progress. Instead of the battle of Clontarf, I was riding across the prairie with the Lone Ranger and Tonto. It was the day our first television set was to arrive.

Free from school at last, we raced up the lane towards home.

Then I saw it! Perched majestically on the chimney pot, its metal spikes reaching towards the heavens. Little shivers of excitement ran up and down my spine.

"The aerial is up already, I wonder if it's come yet?" my young brother said breathlessly.

"Just think, we won't have to run down the wet fields to Mc Connell's to see the Lone Ranger anymore," I chipped in.

We burst into the kitchen, throwing our school bags and coats at our feet. The shelf stood empty to our great disappointment.

"It hasn't come yet," my mother said.

"I wouldn't be a bit surprised if it's not smashed to smithereens, the way the railways throw things around," my father commented from behind his newspaper.

We felt somewhat deflated at this piece of bad news. It was easy to imagine railway porters throwing our precious television onto carriages to get smashed to pieces. "God please don't let this happen," I silently prayed.

Half an hour later the van arrived in the yard. We ran out excitedly, just as the door was opened.

Our fears about the porters throwing it around were soon laid to rest when we caught sight, of the huge crate which must have weighed a ton. It took the might of my father, my oldest brother, Mickey the van driver and Paddy our burly neighbour to lift it off the van.

With the help of a claw-hammer the crate was dismantled. The old rags and straw packing were discarded in endless bundles. Then at last the enormous wooden cabinet appeared out of the straw and rags. The small fourteen inch screen looked lost in its oak surround. But to us it was the most beautiful sight we had ever seen.

Then began the task of hauling it into the house.

"Now lift when I say, careful now," my

brother instructed as all helpers shuffled forward under its weight.

At last it was in place seated on a sturdy table. It was wisely decided unanimously that the shelf was not strong enough to support its weight.

When finally it was wired up and plugged in, we held our breath in anticipation. A loud hissing sound came from it, then a blizzard appeared on the screen.

"The aerial needs adjusting that's all," my big brother said encouragingly. With this all hands went to the street as he climbed the ladder to the aerial. My father tutted and grumbled as he battled with the mountain of hastily discarded packing.

We formed a human chain from the blizzard on the screen to the yard, while my brother twisted and turned the aerial.

"No nothing yet, wait, that's a wee bit better We have the sound now," I shouted as hissing strains of Adam Faith singing 'Poor Me' could be faintly heard.

A little more fine tuning and a picture emerged to our great relief.

"Let joy be unconfined!" said my father mockingly.

We all settled down to watch the Beverly Hillbillies through a light snow flurry, when Paddy O'Neill came in. To our amazement he showed no interest in the television whatsoever.

Instead he began his usual conversation with my father about the weather and the crops. The only difference from other nights was the raised voices. When he got up to go he stopped momentarily in front of the TV.

"Them contraptions will never catch on you know," he said.

# The Oil

We set up shop in the old disused quarry. The carved out ledges, made ideal shelves for a general store. We gathered old tin cans and pebbles, and raided the corn store, which we mentally transformed into brown sugar. When all was ready, it was time to inform our friends, that our store was open for buisness.

Business was brisk for the first day or two. But gradually, disputes began to emerge between shopkeeper and customers.

"What good are stupid old pebbles, instead of sweets? I'm going home," Pat announced.

This trend continued, as one by one, the customers disappeared in search of more exciting pursuits.

A reprieve for the shop came unexpectedly in the guise, of summer relations from afar, who came to visit.

We sat on the sofa in a row as quiet as mice, while they told us about how much we had grown since they last saw us.

"You look more like your Aunt Margaret every day."

"I can't get over how you have grown John."

We smiled angelically at each comment, until our jaws ached.

"Such quiet well mannered wee souls."

And on it went, until our patience and pretence at being 'the good quiet wee souls' ran out.

Two hours later, and still seated on the sofa, John turned to me, and asked the question that was on both our minds. But it was ill timed, his tone too loud, and just by sheer bad luck during a lull in the conversation.

"I wonder how much they will give us?" he asked.

My mother's red face stared in our direction, with a look that withered us. But if our visitors heard, they showed no sign of it, as the conversation resumed as normal.

When at last they bade their farewells, much to our relief and delight, they handed us half a crown each.

When they were out of sight my mother said angrily;

"I have a good mind to take that money from you, you disgraced me."

"Poor wee John has no sense, he didn't mean any harm. And anyway I don't think they heard him,'' I said in his defence.

Ten minutes later we were on our way to Murphy's shop, clutching our half crowns tightly.

"We have enough money for sixty black-jacks,'' John announced, after much finger counting.

"I bet they would all soon come back to the shop if they knew. And if we halved them we would have a hundred and twenty,'' I said.

When word got around that sweets could be bought, with a pebble currency, a brisk trade was resumed. But the black jacks soon ran out, and with no hope of fresh supplies, we opened a bakery. The mud pie production was a great success, and soon rows of them lined the quarry shelves.

But, the brisk trade in mud pies came to an abrupt halt, when Mary Mc Meenan's three year old brother ate the greater part of one.

"Oh, God what will we do. Will he die do you think?'' she asked with terror in her eyes. The mud was still clinging to the side of his face, and his small mouth, turned up at the corners when the mud hit his taste buds.

"Take him into my mother, quick, hurry.''

"Wee Jimmy... he swallowed half a mud pie.

47

Will he die?'' I spluttered frantically, standing the tiny mite on the floor.

"It would take a lot more than a mud pie to kill you, wee man,'' she said with a smile. "But we will have to speed nature up a bit in getting rid of it,'' she added, reaching up to the shelf for the castor oil.

We cringed in sympathy as the spoonfull of foul smelling oil was held to his mouth.

"Swallow it down, and I'll give you a nice spoonful of jam,'' she coaxed.

"Now don't forget to tell your mother that I have given him the castor oil, one dose of it is enough in one day,'' she told Mary before she left.

'Wee Jimmy' grew to over six foot. And each time I saw him from that day on, I was reminded of black jacks, mud pies, and castor oil.

# Emigration

Gaping holes where your
twinkling glass
Once reflected light.
Your once thatched roof
Just a gaping space.

Your garden wall
outlined above
The overgrown briars.
Imagine you as you
once were
The sounds of
children at play.

Your roof space
neatly thatched,
The scent from your
turf fire waffs
Through the air.

Your garden now,
a row of neat
corn stacks
Tightly secured
against winter storm,
And your twinkling
glass windows again;
Reflect the evening
light.

# The New Suit

The long winter nights sometimes passed slowly. We often read, and re-read the same books, fought over card and ludo games, or played draughts to pass the long hours of darkness.

It was times like these that the art of story telling provided an alternative.

"Please daddy, tell us the one about the suit," one of us would ask.

"I'm not in story telling form tonight," he would say. But with a little coaxing he would clear his throat and begin.

The only source of heat in the attic room was from the pipe that led from the pot-bellied stove in the kitchen.

The pipe was a God send in the bitter cold of Robert's first winter in Canada.

But, in summer it only added to the discomfort of the stifling heat.

As he pulled back the covers of his bed he noticed the suit length that hung at the end of Johnnie's bed.

He had hoped that he had given up on the mad idea of making a suit. A wry smile crossed his face as he tumbled into bed.

It seemed hard to believe that only nine months passed since he sailed from Derry.

As he snuggled under the covers for warmth he wondered for the thousandth time why he had come to this God forsaken wilderness.

Johnnie came from Co. Mayo and they met on board the ship. He was just eighteen and was feeling the pangs of homesickness not to mention sea sickness when they encountered their first Atlantic storm of the voyage.

His decision to come to Canada was largely based on the brightly painted posters that suddenly appeared in his home village. 'Come to Canada!' they invited. His fate was sealed the following evening at the village hall. There he viewed pictures of the majestic Rocky Mountains, Niagra Falls and the new towns and cities that were springing up. A land of adventure and opportunity?

Johnnie's young head was filled with a great sense of adventure, not to mention making his fortune while he was about it.

The spring planting awaited them at Robbie

Silcox's homestead; three days journey away on the steam train.

As the train sped along, the wide expanse of prairie lay ahead just broken by the occasional homestead. The hours passed slowly and they dozed to kill the time.

Robbie Silcox was an amazing looking man. His deep set, bright blue eyes peered out from behind hooded eyelids and long bushy eyebrows. The eyebrows looked out of place surrounded by his long, almost white grey beard, and white hair.

He smiled to himself as he remembered their first meeting. How could he forget the sight of this prairie Santa Clause as they stepped from the train? They looked around them taking in the vast, flat plain only broken by the tin roofed shack that served as a station house.

They both looked longingly down the track, their eyes following the fast disappearing train.

Robert walked slowly towards the solitary wagon.

The horse dozed peacefully in the warm sun.

"Hello," he said, "I'm Robert."

"Pleased to meet you!" came the dry reply.

"Jump aboard," Robbie ordered.

He looked back at poor Johnnie standing with one hand in his pocket and the other on his dusty brown suitcase. He looked the picture of misery.

"Come on Johnnie," said Robert, trying to sound lighthearted.

Johnnie looked around him and seemed to decide that there was no where else to go, so he slowly walked towards the wagon and threw his suitcase into the back and jumped aboard himself.

"Get up there," Robbie ordered the horse, and they slowly moved off.

The weeks stretched into months since that day. Hard work and sweat gave them little time to dwell on their homesickness and isolation.

To his great surprise he had grown very fond of old Robbie despite the bad beginning on that first meeting and early days and weeks at Silcox homestead.

The spring ploughing was something he would never forget, walking behind the team of horses, he must have walked a mile for each furrow he ploughed.

When quitting time came they were both muscle sore and weary and had just enough energy to eat supper and crawl into bed.

Each letter from home brought new pangs of longing for home and family, even though the news was pretty outdated by the time it arrived.

Winter brought more leisure time, and only served to increase their discontent.

Robbie Silcox was only too aware of this.

With spring not too far off, he made extra efforts to keep the two young Irishmen until the crops were planted.

Johnnie's clothes were completely threadbare and after much deliberation he produced his suit length, all the way from Cong, Co. Mayo.

The cloth lay spread across the table.

"Are you sure about this?" Robert asked, the scissors poised above the cloth at the ready.

"I'm sure," came Johnnie's reply.

No sooner had the words been spoken than the cutting began. As each piece of cloth was carefully cut into size the old pieces of tattered suit were discarded one by one; the pattern no longer needed.

"It was a good idea of mine to use the old suit as a pattern," Johnnie bragged.

"Yeah," Robert agreed, not taking his eyes from the task he grudgingly undertook.

"If you are as good with a needle and thread as I am at this job, you will have all the women in Manitoba after you!" Robert joked.

Johnnie looked doubtful at the mention of the needle and thread. Covering a hole with a patch was one matter, but sewing an entire suit was another! And now the cutting was done, he knew there was no turning back.

Part of the bargain with Robbie included the forthcoming visit to town; just ten days away.

Johnnie had a lot of needle work to do if the suit was to be finished by then.

"Why did we come to this isolated wilderness; fifty miles from nowhere?" Johnnie grumbled, the sewing needle poised in mid air, his other hand massaging his aching back.

"From where I'm sitting now Cong, Co. Mayo is the centre of civilization. At least you could find a tailor to make you a damned suit when every stitch you possess is threadbare."

Johnnie spent hours in his room sewing his new suit together.

Marion invited him to work in the kitchen,

"It's warmer in here and the light is better," she coaxed.

But Johnnie wouldn't budge from his attic room, he just couldn't let them see him sewing, he couldn't bear the smart comments that was sure to come from Robbie and Robert.

Robbie poked the potbellied stove, then threw in some more logs, he lit his pipe and was just about to settle down when the door opened. All three looked towards the door.

Johnnie walked in from the shadows of the hallway. He was wearing the suit.

"Well, what do you think?" he asked, walking towards the centre of the floor close to the lamp.

All three were speechless, as they took in the figure before them.

The shoulders were lopsided, the left shoulder puckered up to a point making him look as if he had a pointed rock underneath the cloth.

The left lapel of the jacket was long and puckered, the right one short and puckered.

As their eyes wandered down toward the sleeve they saw that the puckers became more like pleats.

One sleeve covered his knuckles, and, the other barely reached his wrist.

The trousers resembled ankle length plus fours, they seemed to billow at the knees and taper in above his ankles. Marion stifled a giggle, and soon the other two joined in.

Their laughter got louder and Johnnie's face reddened with anger.

Marion flew out of the kitchen. But try as they might they couldn't control their laughter, despite Johnnie's fury at them. Marion waltzed back in through the door banging the sides as she came in carrying a large mirror.

"Look Johnnie," she commanded, propping the mirror in front of him.

He viewed himself for a few seconds. Then he began to smile, then giggles that lengthened into long peals of laughter.

Robert and Johnnie returned to their native

heath two years later.

It goes without saying that neither of them took up tailoring as a means of livelihood.

# Iron Wheels

The sound of a motor car horn awoke me from a drowsy sleep. From the upstairs window I watched my young brother alight from a gleaming white car. He glanced back at it admiringly, as he headed for the door.

"Well, what do you think of it?" he greeted me with a broad grin, and a proud nod in the direction of the shiny white hunk of metal.

"Want to come for a run in it?" he asked, before I had time to comment.

Later dressed and ready to go I gave my shoes a quick once over before stepping into the spotless interior.

Speeding along the Berkshire countryside, I smiled to myself as I remembered his first mode of transport.

"What you grinning at?" he said, glancing sideways at me. "I was just remembering Neddy," I replied with a strong note of nostalgia in my voice. Transported back to the farm, and Donegal with vivid clarity, I recalled the events of his long ago most prized means of transport.

My father was seated in his usual chair by the fire. The smoke from his pipe wafting above the newspaper he was reading.

"Daddy, do you think you could afford to buy me a donkey?" We could hear my father sigh from behind the newspaper.

"Not again son, sure we have been over this yesterday."

"It wouldn't cost that much, and a donkey would be useful for a lot of things," he reasoned.

"The last thing we need about the place is a stupid donkey," William, our older brother piped up.

"You shut up and mind your own buisness," he stormed, his small grubby face looking close to tears, as he ran from the kitchen.

My father folded his newspaper carefully. Then looking across at my mother as she baked bread at the kitchen table, he cleared his throat;

"It wouldn't exactly break the bank to get the wee fellow a donkey. You are only that age once," he said, looking at my mother anxiously as he awaited her response.

"Oh, all right if it will give us a bit of peace."

Once the decision was made we lost no time
in acquiring Neddy. We walked four miles
along dark lonely lane-ways to find the man
who sold the donkeys.

"Four pounds ten, and not a penny more,"
my mother said while we held our breath. At
last they shook hands on the deal and Neddy
was all Johns. His small curly head was just
visible in the darkness as he led Neddy proudly
home walking just a few feet ahead of us.

In the lower meadow we watched John from
the kitchen window as he was thrown from
Neddy's back unceremoniously.

"He's a young donkey. Not broken by the
looks of it," my father remarked.

"He'll break his neck yet. That brute will kill
him," my mother sighed.

"Not a bit of it will kill him, he will soon
master him. You'll see."

But my mother wasn't convinced. She pulled
the curtains to avoid watching the rodeo in the
meadow.

Neddy eventually gave in, we watched him
camly canter, trot and eventually walk placidly
around the field with the small figure seated
firmly on his back.

"Daddy do you think you could make me a
wee cart for Neddy?" he asked cautiously one
evening.

"I was waiting for that," my father said, without glancing from behind the newspaper.

After a short silence and some throat clearing, John ventured. "Well, could you?"

"I suppose I could try. But you will have to help me. And it will have to be made with whatever we can find lying around. New timber is too expensive," he concluded.

We willingly agreed, and we set to work on the manufacture of Neddy's cart, gathering all the bits of discarded wood we could find lying around. With hammer and nails my father set to work. Soon a box shape began to emerge as we watched in admiration.

"I don't know a damn where we are going to find wheels for it," he said as the last nail was hammered home.

After an hour of searching my father sat on a rock, scratching his head as he pondered on the problem. The old horse cart wheels we found were far too big. Then his eyes settled on the old reaper, long discarded and lying in a rusting heap at the head of the field.

"Aye, it just might do the job," he said to himself.

When the old harness was ready we eventually yoked Neddy to his new cart. At first the noise from the iron wheels caused alarm to Neddy. When he had been led around the yard a few times with much reassurance, he got used to the noisy contraption following behind him.

As Neddy and cart plodded along the lane-ways, John's imagination ran riot. He became the lone ranger and Wyatt Earp from the TV westerns all rolled into one. A gorse or heather fire meant Indian attack was imminent.

"Get down, Indians," he would shout. On these occasions he was leading a wagon train, heading west.

As I was fast approaching the grand old age of twelve, I was becoming more and more reluctant to travel in Neddy's cart. "What if we meet someone from school? Just go on your own."

"Please come with me. We will go on the bog road, never meet a sinner on that road," he reassured me. As a precaution, and by good fortune, I took a rug on my final trip on Neddy's cart.

To my horror on the bog road coming towards us I recognised an older boy from the neighbourhood, for whom I was beginning to develop a strong crush. Diving for cover under the rug I vowed never again would I be seen in Neddy's cart.

"It drives smoothly dosn't it?" John asked as the white car came to a halt.

"Aye, it's a grand car. But I wish I was back in Neddy's cart!"

# The Cuckoo Clock

The snow came silently while we slept, and we awoke to find a white, snow-covered landscape. The snow was still falling thick and fast by school time, and it was decided that we should have the day off.

At eleven o'clock Aunt Bea moved over to her window seat to wait for the postman as usual.

"Poor Eddy will have a struggle this morning," she said, her eyes glued to the distant road. Her white hair was pinned up in a neat bun, and perched sedately on top, her black beret with the little tassel on it.

She had reached the grand old age of eighty, and could still walk the two miles to the village for her pension each Friday. With unfailing eyesight she was able to knit our sweaters without the aid of spectacles. Reading and letter writing were her other pass times.

"I should have had a letter from Mary before

now. It must be all of six weeks since I wrote to her. And I was sure that my cuckoo clock would have come weeks ago," she said, dropping her eyes to her knitting again.

"Oh Lord! Eddy's down, and the letters are scattered everywhere," she suddenly shrieked. "Run, quick, one of you, and help him. Poor Eddy, he's too old to be out delivering mail on a day like this."

John and I scrambled into our coats, and made off down the lane at speed, to rescue Eddy. As we neared the spot where the unfortunate Eddy came a cropper, he suddenly sprang to his young and sprightly feet.

"We should have known it was you up to your tricks again," John said, as William came towards us with a broad grin. Behind him lay a trail of old newspaper squares scattered in the snow.

"Was she watching? Did she think it was Eddy?" he asked us still grinning.

"Aye, she thought it was Eddy alright. I wouldn't show my nose for a while if I were you," John warned, as the three of us walked back up the lane through the snow.

"You are a right bad rascal, playing a trick like that on me," she scolded when he came in, "And there was me thinking poor Eddy might have broken a leg."

"I just couldn't resist it. I knew you would be watching," he said with a chuckle.

An hour or so later, Eddy made his appearance.

"It's a day neither fit for man nor beast," he announced shaking the snow from his coat as he came into the kitchen carrying a parcel.

As my mother busied herself making him hot tea, we set about the parcel. Out of the wood shavings and cardboard emerged Aunt Bea's cuckoo clock.

"It's all in one piece anyway, nothing broken," she commented with a broad smile of pleasure.

After the instructions were carefully read, and understood, the clock was carefully hung on the wall. We waited patiently as the hour of one came closer. Then on the dot, the little wooden doors sprang open, and out popped the bird, "cuckoo! cuckoo!" it chanted loud and clear. Aunt Bea beamed with pleasure. "Isn't the cuckoo a wee dote," she exclaimed. We all nodded in agreement.

The snow didn't let up that afternoon, and we became bored and restless. We finally went outside to play in the shed. John began target practice with his treasured air gun. "Another bulls eye," he shouted triumphantly at intervals.

"I'm sick of that flipping gun, that's all you seem to want to do anymore," I complained as I headed for the house again. In the kitchen the hour was approaching three, and Aunt Bea's eyes were held firmly on the clock. "Cuckoo, cuckoo, cuckoo," rang out again much to her delight.

As the weeks passed the clock was beginning to grate on the nerves of everyone apart from its proud owner. The "wee dote" became "that damned cuckoo," especially as the hours grew to high numbers. Ten cuckoos became just too much for the nerves to bear.

One night in February, the family sat around the fire. Only the soothing sounds of knitting needles clicking and newspaper rustling disturbed the silence. None of us were aware of the impending disaster, as the hour of ten o'clock drew near.

The wooden doors on the clock opened. "Cuc....." and then BANG! All eyes were suddenly on John, where he sat on the sofa; the air gun still poised in mid air. The cuckoo hung limply from its perch, suddenly silent.

"You young rascal, you shot my poor wee cuckoo," Bea cried out in anguish. John dived for the door, my father grabbing the gun before he disappeared outside.

"I'm hiding this gun, where you won't get
your hands on it again," he called after him.

William set to work at once on the repair of
"the wee dote." When the intricate operation
was finished, we waited again as the hour drew
near. The doors opened, and out popped a
lopsided cuckoo, sitting precariously on his
perch, " ook, ...ook, ...ook, ...ook," he crooked
miserably.

"Good lad, you fixed it," Aunt Bea said in
obvious delight.

"This is one occasion when loss of hearing
seems to be a blessing," my father said quietly.

# The Collection

The spring sun shone brightly through the curtains on Sunday morning.

"It's time to get up for church," mother announced. Half an hour later, dressed in our Sunday best, we were each handed sixpence for the collection.

"Behave yourselves. And no glowering behind you in church. You are the oldest, so you are in charge," she warned me, as we went out the door.

And so we set off on the two mile walk to the village church.

"I wish I had two threepence pieces, sixpence is two much for the plate," John said when we had walked a mile or so.

"You will put the sixpence in the plate, like you were told," I said crossly. "That sixpence is God's money."

"God would be glad enough to get half of it. And anyway you can't boss me around," he scoffed.

As we passed Josie Durkin's house a row was in progress, between herself and her nearest neighbour, a formidable widow woman.

"Sunday is no day to be fighting, I know, but if that man of yours dosn't put up better fences, and keep them cows of his out of my fields, I'll get the Guards on him," the widow screeched angrily.

"Go on then do what you like you old tarter. Not much wonder that husband of yours popped his clogs before his time," Josie spat back. This last remark obviously hit its target. The widow stormed off muttering about what 'a wicked woman' Josie was. "And on Sunday morning too," she added with contempt, shaking her fist at her opponent, as she went.

The row over, we walked on at a faster pace. The second bell rang out in the belfry just as we reached the outskirts of the village. John ran on ahead to Kelly's shop. He came back with a pout on his face.

"It's closed," he said, with disappointment.

Sunday worship was drawing to a close. As we sang the final hymn, Harry, the dark suited, stern faced sexton, reached our pew, and reverently presented the collection plate. I put my sixpenny bit in with the other coins. Then it was Johns turn. He too put his sixpence into the plate but, to my horror, he immediatly took threepence out. "My change," he whispered.

"Ouch," he groaned when my sharp elbow dug into his ribs. During the walk home he shared the sweets with me, but only because I threatened to tell.

Ten years on, I sat in the same pew for the funeral service of the sexton. The clergyman preached at great length about Harry's devotion to God, and his work at the church.

As he droned on, a rhyme I once read somewhere came into my head.

I cannot praise the preachers eyes,
I never saw his glance devine,
He always shuts them when he prays,
And when he preaches he shuts mine.

His next words made me sit up and take notice.

"Harry had a keen sense of humour, although he didn't always make this side of his nature obvious. He laughed heartily, as he told me the following little jem just a few weeks ago," he went on. "It was about the church collection. Apparently, a wee lad once put sixpence in the collection plate, and then searched around until he found threepence change, while his older sister looked on in horror."

# Shore

The chilly bite of a winter dawn on the deserted
shore
Only my own footprints on the hard firm sand.
How many prints of those that trod before me?
Have been long since washed clean
Ahead of the ceaselessly, timeless rushing tide.

# Forever Young

William was the oldest member of the family. And being bigger, older and wiser than the rest, he became the figure of our hero worship. He was greatly in tune with nature and the wildlife of his surroundings.

The surrounding countryside was at that time alive with rabbits, much to the annoyance of the farmers, for they played havoc with the crops. He became an expert at catching them, and as a result of this rabbit was frequently on our menu. However, you can have just about too much of anything. And so we had to let this fact be known without causing too much offence. That is where, a prayer that became known as the 'Magilligan Grace' came in handy. One or other of us would recite it at the table;

For rabbits hot and rabbits cold
For rabbits young and rabbits old
For rabbits tender and rabbits tough
We thank thee Lord we've had enough."

On a cold raw spring morning I was up bright
and early. I watched William put on his boots.

"Where are you going?" I asked him.

"To check on the sheep, at the port."

"Would you take me with you?"

"I might have to walk for miles over the hill.
You would be tired in no time, and I'll have
enough to do without worrying about you.
Three or four of the ewes are due to lamb, and
they will probably have broken out."

"Why do they break out when they are due
to lamb?" I asked.

"Hill sheep have some sort of instinct, to get
away from the rest of the flock at lambing time.
The foxes got three lambs this year already,"
he added.

"I could help you to look for them. And I
could come home by myself if I got tired." I
said in my sweetest voice.

"Come on then, but don't complain about
being tired," he warned as we set off.

We trudged over the hill and along the tops
of the cliffs, in search of the missing ewes. My
nine year old legs soon began to tire as we
walked further, and further over the rough
terrain.

"I can't go any further, my legs ache
awful," I wailed.

"Didn't I warn you this would happen," he
said in annoyance. "The only thing for it, is for

you to wait here until I get back. Now, don't move from here or you'll get lost. Sit down under this whin bush for shelter,'' he suggested. With tears in my eyes I walked over and sat under the bush.

"Don't move from where you are, remember,'' he warned again as he walked away.

Alone fear began to take over my thoughts, What if he doesn't come back, I wouldn't be able to find my way back home? The near silence was deafening, the only sound came from the lonely sounding cry of the gulls.

At first I saw the Hawthorn stick as it came to rest in front of my feet. With mounting terror, my eyes travelled up from the black boots and the long grey coat, finally coming to rest on the head. Wisps of greying hair escaped from a green wollen hat, framing a leathery wind-beaten face. Steel grey eyes stared back at me. 'My God, a witch, I am done for' I thought frantically.

Then in a female voice, she asked.

"Do you think I'm a witch or something?''

This question seemed to clearly confirm my fears. If she knew what I was thinking, she must truly be a witch. Then she spoke again and dispelled my fears.

"William told me I would find you here.

Come back to the house with me, he will call for you there when he finds the sheep.''

I followed her along a heather path, followed in turn by two dogs a three-legged cat and at the rear an elderly ewe with one horn. The dwelling at last came into sight, tucked neatly under a rocky hill.

''Come on in and I'll get you something to eat. I'll boil you a couple of fresh eggs, you're bound to be hungry after all the walking,'' she said as she opened the door.

The kitchen had a cosy warmth about it, a turf fire burned brightly in the hearth, and an unusal spicy scent permeated the air. Woven baskets of all shapes and sizes hung around the walls, and near the fireplace a long shelf bulged with books. ''The eggs are ready, come and sit at the table,'' she said.

As my fear of her subsided, I suddenly realized I was hungry, and ate the eggs and homemade bread with relish.

''William is a grand lad,'' she said. ''He always calls in when he's passing. I don't get many visitors, the local people think I'm a bit odd, eccentric, you might say. But William and myself have our love of nature, and our love of books in common. Aye, he's a grand young lad,'' she repeated.

''Don't you get lonely?'' I asked.

''So you have a voice,'' she commented with

a glint in her grey eyes.

"As far as being lonely is concerned, the answer is no. Sure, how would I be lonely when, I have my animals for company, and natures wild creatures all around. No, thank God I'm not lonely."

Just then a tapping noise came from a tea chest in the corner. Taking the cover off the chest, she reached in and took out a bird. "So, you're getting better," she said in gentle tones. "It's a skylark, broken leg, I had to splice it, but he will soon be ready for freedom again."

A short time later William returned with a lamb under each arm, and the ewes following behind. I bade a reluctant farewell. "Come back when them legs of yours grow a bit," she called after me.

"Well, how did you get on with Josie Mc Ateer then?" he asked as we walked along.

"I like her, she's strange, but nice. Mind you, she scared the hell out of me when I first saw her. I really thought she was a witch!" His laughter echoed through the glen.

"Josie is a wise woman, a very wise woman," he said. "I better not tell her you thought she was a witch."

"Oh, thats all right, she knows already, because she asked me if I thought she was a witch. She can read thoughts you see." Again he laughed and said as he ruffled my hair;

"I think you're a bit of a wee witch yourself."

I gave him an admiring gaze, that said, "my hero." Ten springs were to come and go before I would next see Josie.

The warm May morning sun glistened on the sea as I set off over the same cliffs towards Josie's cottage. A strong need to return drove me onwards. It had been exactly one year, since Williams life had suddenly and tragically been cut short, as the result of a road accident.

When my mother heard where I was going she warned;

"She may not welcome you, they say she dosn't take kindly to strangers."

"Maybe not, but I won't be a stranger."

She seemed to sense my arrival, as I came close to the house. I saw her standing at the gable. She looked feeble and a little stooped, but her facial appearance had not changed at all. She almost ran to greet me, "I somehow knew you would come," she said putting her arms around me. I could feel her tears fall down her leathery old face as they mingled with mine.

"Come on in, I will put on the kettle," she said with a soft smile, making no attempt to hide her tears.

As we drank the tea she spoke again;

"On the day I heard about his death, I could only sit and weep. Then I walked out to Binnin cliff, and I had a sudden feeling of peace sweep over me." Her grey eyes looked deeply into mine before she went on;

"I knew in that instant, that William's new home is a place of wide open spaces, where he can roam free. And to me, and all who knew and loved him. He will be forever young."

For the first time in twelve long, grief striken months, I was at peace.

"Now that your legs have grown he sent you back here all by yourself," the old woman said suddenly, once again, she had read my thoughts.

# Horror In The Barn

The cold February wind blew from the north
east, bringing sleet and rain out of a grey dark
sky. As I peddled the bicycle towards home,
out of the evening gloom the poster on the
sycamore tree caught my attention. I got off the
bike to get a closer look, almost toppling over
the heavy box of groceries from the parcel
carrier in my haste.

**FLANNIGAN'S TRAVELLING PICTURE
SHOW WILL BE SCREENING
'THE SINKING OF THE TITANIC'
AT REARDON'S BARN ON FRIDAY
NIGHT AT 8.00 P.M.
ADMISSION SIXPENCE.**

With our sixpences safely in our pockets, we
set off through the dark laneways to Reardon's
barn.

We could hear the sound of the generator clearly in the still frosty air as we approached.

Sean Flannigan was standing with his back to the turf fire when we went in.

"It's a cold night, come over to the fire and warm yourselves. You're a bit early. The show won't be starting for a wee while yet," he greeted us.

We handed over our sixpences to the man at the door, warmed our hands at the fire, and sat down on the long stool at the front, close to the big screen.

The barn had been swept clean for the occasion, and ten long former church pews lined the floor facing the screen.

Soon the barn was full, and excited anticipation filled the air. Eight o'clock had come and gone, but there was still no sign of the show starting. Impatient feet began to shuffle on the floor, and impatient sighs grew louder.

Then the man who had collected our money stood up in front of the screen, first clearing his throat he began in a loud voice,

"Ladies and Gentlemen, boys and girls, I am terribly sorry, but due to unforeseen circumstances we are unable to screen the film advertised tonight."

"Aaaaah's" of disappointment echoed through the audience.

He waved his hands in the air for silence as he began again.

"As I said, although we are unable to show you the film we advertised, I'm sure you will enjoy the one we are about to show you just as much. Now, settle down and enjoy; Count Dracula."

As the film got underway, the suspense soon began to mount.

The beautiful girl lay on the bed, her long hair spread out on the pillow, as the lace curtains swayed gently in the breeze. Then just as Dracula appeared with fangs bared, the screen went blank.

"Just a slight technical difficulty, we will have it fixed in no time," the same man announced, while we all sat biting our nails in impatient suspense.

When the film was over, we all filed out into the dark night for the long walk home. Little conversation passed between us; Dracula's terrifying deeds were still held fast in our minds, as we trudged through the darkness.

Later tucked up safely in bed, sleep came fast, but not for long. I awoke in terror a short time later, just as Dracula's fangs were about to dig into my neck in search of blood.

When this nightmare had repeated itself

again, and again, I abandoned the bed for the cold night air, as a means of ensuring that I was fully conscious, and the dreaded Dracula was locked away in his Transylvanian castle.

Something warm and hairy touched my arm. I jumped in alarm.

But fear was short lived. "It's only you Lassie," I muttered in relief as she licked my hand. "Go on back into the barn, go on." But she didn't budge.

Then the idea took shape, the faithful old dog would protect me from all comers, including Dracula. As she followed me into the bedroom the memory of Mother's words came back. "That dog is full of fleas, she is not allowed into the house until I get some DDT for her."

"What harm will a few wee fleas do compared with Dracula," I whispered as Lassie snuggled up to me comfortingly.

# Hospitality

The early morning mist cleared leaving a clear blue summer sky. The day stretched ahead of us, and for once we had no plans for the long daylight hours ahead.

"How about going down to the village?" Kate suggested as she pumped the tyre of the bicycle.

"We have no money. And anyway I'm tired of the village. Have you no other suggestions?"

She shook her head slowly. Then her face lit up as an idea sprang to light.

"How about going down to Cruckheeny, to visit my father's cousins?"

"I've never been down there. But it's somewhere to go I suppose," I said, with little enthusiasm.

We cycled down into the unfamiliar glen, in search of Kate's cousins. The first call was to a neatly thatched cottage, with a breath taking view of the surrounding hills and the sea. Kate knocked on the door and immediately lifted the latch. Once inside Kate called out in a loud voice. "Are you in Mary?" But there was only silence, apart from the loud ticking of the grandmother clock.

"She must be out in the garden or somewhere," Kate suggested.

"We will be off then," I said, anxious to get away from the dark silent cottage. But just then the door opened and Mary appeared in the doorway. A tall thin woman in late middle age; she stared at us without recognition for a few seconds.

"Is it wee Kate Mc Laughlin?" she asked with a slightly puzzled look.

"That's right. We thought it was a nice day for visiting relatives," Kate blurted out a little nervously.

"Well good for you, aye good for you. I'm delighted to welcome you both. Now let me get a closer look at you.

"You're Johnnie Mc Ateer's daughter, I would know you on them anywhere," she announced to my amazement.

When we had listened to all the news of the family, and neighbours and had devoured half a dozen of her home-made scones, we made our farewells, and moved on to the next cousin.

In the next house we ate and drank again, before going on to the next call.

"Welcome to you both, come in and sit yourselves down."

Miss Mulcahy greeted us from a plush arm chair.

"Are you enjoying your holidays?" Kate asked her.

"Oh, yes, teaching is a very stressful occupation you know. We need the long summer break to recover our resources."

She got up from her plush chair and went to the cupboard. We watched as she poured two glassfuls of golden liquid.

"Lucozade, it's very refreshing," she said as she handed each of us a glassfull. Then back she went to the cupboard.

This time she brought back a plate-full of chocolate biscuits. Although our stomach's were full almost to bursting point, we just could not refuse these rare and delicious delicacies that were being offered to us, and so once again we ate and drank. Once outside we waddled along the lane wheeling the bikes.

"I have a pain in my stomach," I wailed. "I hope you have no more cousins to visit or I will burst for sure."

"There is two more, but we will leave them for another day."

We slowly left Cruckheeny with our overlaiden stomachs slowing us down almost to a stand-still.

We reached home just in time for tea.

# The Moving Chair

We waited in the grey morning drizzle by the
stone pillars, as Eoghan Flynn's coffin was
carried out of the house.

"He died in his sleep, a good way to go," an
old woman close by said in low tones, while
others muttered in agreement.

But, as we looked at his wife Mary-Anne's
sunken face full of shock and grief, we could
think of nothing good about his going.

We shuffled along slowly in the wake of the
shoulder high coffin.

"Poor uncle Eoghan, he was good to us,"
Sara's small quivering voice came out of the
gloom as she moved up beside us.

"And to think that only two nights ago he
was playing cards with us," John added
solemnly.

We stood at the grave-side until the last
shovelfull of earth covered him. As we turned
to go we could hear Mary-Anne's muffled sobs

in the still damp air. Then an old woman began quietly reciting in Irish.

"Dá bhfóirfeadh orm an bás
Beadh dherbh m'fhailte fá na
chómhair!

"Come on let's go home," John said quietly, anxious to be away from the sad morbid grave-side.

Barely a word was spoken between us as we walked home through the drizzle, each in their own way trying to come to terms with the loss of an old friend and neighbour.

Then John broke the silence. "They all keep saying that he was young, but how could he be young when he was forty years older than me," he reasoned.

"That still only makes him fifty, and fifty isn't old my father says," Sara rounded a little crossly.

"I don't care what your father says, it seems old to me."

"John, I wish to God you would just be quiet for once. Can't you see you are annoying Sara, and her uncle not cold in the grave yet." I said, giving him a withering look. With that he sauntered on ahead, kicking pebbles as he went.

Mary-Anne's door remained firmly closed in the days that followed despite the much improved weather.

"My father says we must go in and see her as usual. He says she will be very lonely." Sara said as we passed the cottage. "Will we go in now and get it over with? She asked the rest, with pleading eyes.

We lifted the latch and went in. Mary-Anne sat and stared into space, seeming hardly aware of our presence. Eoghan's chair sat empty and sad, and his pipe still sat on the mantelpiece.

Sara cleared her throat. "How are you?"

"Lost, lonely... grieving," her voice trailed away in a long low sigh, her eyes staring blankly at the empty chair.

A few nervous coughs later, and we bade her farewell promising to return on the following day.

A week had passed without any sign of improvement, when we decided to take action.

"It's the chair. She sits staring at it all day," was the unanimous conclusion. "When we get her out of the house for Mass in the morning we will move it, and the pipe," Sara said with enthusiasm.

The following morning we watched the black coated figure, with head bent, walk slowly from the house and up the brae.

"Come on let's get moving," Sara said when Mary-Anne disappeared from sight.

Once inside no time was lost in moving the

offending chair. It took three of us to carry it out of the kitchen and down to the lower room. The pipe was wrapped in newspaper and hidden in the bottom drawer of the tallboy.

Sara glanced around the kitchen before going towards the door, ''Mission accomplished, better get going before she gets back,''

''We will wait behind the pillar; just to hear what her reaction will be when she discovers the chair has moved.''

''She's coming already, she's at the top of the brae,'' John shouted down to us from high in the tree by the gate.

Tired of waiting we were about to leave our hiding place when Mary-Anne made a sudden appearance.

Her brown eyes flashed with anger and indignation.

''How dare you, how dare you, go into my home and move my furniture when I'm out. Just you wait until I tell your parents about what you have been up to.''

''We only moved it because we thought it would help. You sat staring at it all the time,'' Sara interrupted close to tears.

''Do you seriously think, that moving Eoghan's chair would stop me grieving for him?'' her red face blazed; now only inches from us, as she waved an accusing finger.

At last she turned and marched off towards

the house defiantly.

With sagging spirits we went our seperate ways vowing to give Mary-Anne a wide berth in the coming days.

On the following Monday morning we noticed that Mary-Anne's door stood open. We walked on quietly past, hoping to avoid her. But she had obviously been waiting for us. "I want to talk to you, it will only take a minute," she called from the door. Had we not been so apprehensive, we would have recognised the change in her attitude.

"I'm not going to bite. I have something I need to say to you all." The chair had not been put back in its place much to our surprise.

"I'm sorry for the things I said to you the other day. You were right, I was feeling sorry for myself. You made me see that, and I thank you. The night after you moved the chair and pipe, I had a vivid dream about Eoghan, at least I think it was a dream. Anyhow, he told me to pull myself together, and that I should be grateful that you all cared enough to do what you did. Now off you go to school."

She stroked the tops of our heads in turn as we went out the door. We glanced back at her from the gateway, and saw her wipe a tear from her eye.

Twenty five years later I sat in Sara's living room looking through old photographs, and reminiscing about our youth when I spied the chair.

"Is that Eoghan's chair?"

"It is that, Aunt Mary-Anne left it to me in her will." Just looking at the big wooden framed chair brought Eoghan's presence loomed largely into the room. The burn marks on the wood were visible scars of the hot tobacco ash that had frquently sprayed from his pipe. "Be careful with that pipe, you'll burn the place down one of these days," Mary-Anne's voice echoed back through time.

Sara disturbed my thought as she handed me a parcel.

"This is the reason why I wanted you here tonight. Go on open it," she urged.

I stared at the beautifully made wooden object; an exact replica of Eoghan's chair.

"Aunt Mary-Anne made one of these for each of you. It was a talent she discovered in her old age."

"She must have used the remainder of his tobacco to add the burn marks," I added, with misty eyes.

# City Friends And Petticoats

August was in many ways the happiest month of the year for us. The two storey, stone farmhouse, which stood at the top of our lane, remained empty and sad for eleven months of the year.

The family had left the farm, and moved away to the city in the mid fifties. Their departure left a void in our neighbourhood. But our early childhood friendships endured the passage of time. We corresponded throughout the year, while we waited for the August holidays.

In early July we descended on the old house with scrubbing brushes and soap. The spiders and insects, used as they had become to having the house to themselves, darted for cover ahead of the onslaught of the suds and hot water.

Then came the grand day of their arrival, and the fun for us children began. We roamed far and wide, at least as far as our legs, or if we were lucky a bicycle could carry us.

Mother's new bicycle sat in the shed, all shiny and bright. Kate and I looked at it admiringly. "I wonder if she would lend it, now that you are here?" I said to Kate.

"Mind you she did warn us not to dare ask to borrow it. We wrecked the last three bikes she had, you see," I explained.

In the kitchen, in my most pleading voice I said,

"Do you think we could borrow your new bike for a wee while, to go to the village?"

"Now, what did I tell you about asking to borrow my bicycle?" she asked, turning around from the table where she was working.

"We would take good care of it, and we wouldn't be long, please."

"I'll lend it on one condition; only one of you at a time. No giving lifts on the parcel carrier. Take John's wee bike, then you can take it in turns to ride mine. We nodded our agreement to her conditions.

"Remember it has a back peddling brake," she called after us as we were going out the door.

Half an hour later we were on our way to the village, dressed in our cotton summer frocks worn over stiff net petticoats, which make the bottom half of us stand out like parachutes in mid air. But, we were fourteen years old, and believed that we represented the ultimate in grown up sophistication, at the dawning of 1960.

"I'm not going to be seen in the village, riding this wee bike," Kate's voice came from behind.

"Well neither am I. Come on, we will double up on mothers bike. She won't find out," I said, sounding more confident of my statement than I felt.

At the top of the big brae I balanced myself on the parcel carrier, while Kate took the controls.

The rest of the way was all down hill. Suddenly there they were; the road was filled with Molloy's cows on their way home to be milked.

"Oh, God," Kate screeched in terror as she struggled to find the brakes on the handle-bars.

"The back peddling brake," I yelled.

But the warning came too late. We had hit the ditch and were entangled in the hawthorn hedge and barbed wire before we knew it.

"Are you all right?" Sean Molloy's voice seemed to come from a great distance. He helped to pull us out by the arms as we cried out in pain. Our legs and arms came off worst, the blood oozed out from every puncture the thorns and barbed wire had made. But far worse, as far as we were concerned, was the torn petticoats.

Then suddenly Kate said in alarm, "Oh lord help us, your mother's bike." We could only stare in speechless horror, at what had been my mothers pride and joy. The front wheel was buckled and the mudguard stood out like a spike from the tyre.

We limped home carrying the bike, our torn frocks and petticoats hanging in tangled strips, and our hearts heavy.

"I specifically told you, not to ride on the parcel carrier," she shouted at us.

"I'm sorry," I said tearfully.

"Look at the state of you both. Let me get a closer look at those cuts. You could both have been killed," she added with a shake of her head. With warm water, and cotton wool she cleaned and bound our wounds with tenderness.

"Are you not still furious about your bike?" I asked in a small voice.

"Of course I'm still furious. But bikes can be mended easy enough," she said ruffling my hair with her free hand. "But don't ever ask for my bike again."

"Do you think it would be possible to fix the petticoats?" Kate asked in a wee quiet voice, thinking ahead to the dance in the village hall.

"Well, of all the... take them off, and get my sewing box. I'll see what I can do," she said with an amused grin.

The following day the two petticoats hung on the line. We were delighted with the repairs, but they needed to be a bit stiffer, in order to create the right effect.

"I read somewhere that sugar is better than starch for stiffening nylon net," Kate said.

"We'll try it then. I'll get some sugar from the house, and we can soak them in it."

Back on the line after the sugar treatment, we were thrilled with the result. "As stiff as pokers," I said in delight.

At last Friday evening came, and with all the usual warnings about being on our best behaviour we set off for the village hall on foot, petticoats swinging.

The holiday-makers from Scotland were first on the dance floor. We watched them nervously from a corner at first.

Then two young lads from our neighbourhood came and asked us to dance. As the dance progressed, and our bodies warmed up with the exertion, the skin on our legs began to stick together. Kate nudged me on the dance floor, with one hand covering the side of her mouth to avoid being overheard, she hissed, "the sugar has melted."

With that we made a hasty retreat, leaving our sophisticated image in tatters once again!

# The Stranger

He just seemed to suddenly appear in our midst as though he had fallen from midair. A tall lean man, with a leathery weather beaten face wearing a broad brimmed brown hat. In spite of the best efforts of the locals to strike up a conversation with him, he remained aloof and silent.

"It looks like rain again," Brian the grocer commented to the stranger.

"Mmmm!" he muttered, his sharp blue eyes staring back at him coldly.

"He's an odd ball that if I ever saw one, might as well try and strike up a conversation with the pot," Brian commented to us when he went out.

As the weeks passed he ceased to be the topic of conversation in the neighbourhood, and was left to his silent alien existence.

A few weeks later we heard that he had bought an old derelict house in the far glen.

"That place will suit him nicely. There's not even a road into it," Brian commented to a customer one Saturday night within our earshot.

When we met at the corner the following evening we decided to go and suss him out, from the safety of the hill behind the old house.

A thin wood smoke wafted from his chimney. Then we saw him seated on a wicker chair outside the door, smoking a pipe.

"He has a gun, look, it's propped up against the wall. Maybe he's a bank robber or a murderer," John said his eyes dancing as his furtive imagination got into action.

But our daily vigil revealed nothing about the stranger as the summer turned to autumn. Slowly one by one we tired of watching his boring repetitive movements and ceased to play detective.


In the middle of December we returned to the far glen in search of Christmas holly. When the sacks were full, and we were ready to go John's voice rang out in panic through the still air.

"The hat.... the hat, he's lying on the path, nearly dead," he panted excitedly from the top of a rock.

Dropping the sacks we followed him, and there was the stranger lying in the mossy wet grass, his face grey, as his breath came in noisy gasps.

Between the four of us we managed to help him into the house and lay him on the bed. His muttering was incoherent.

"Go up for your Mary, she's a nurse she'll know what to do. The rest of you, get a fire lit," Hannah ordered, taking charge of the situation.

When Mary arrived she took one look at him.

"He's in a bad way, he needs a doctor fast," she pronounced. "Go down for Doctor Sullivan, and tell him to come as quick as possible. Go on all of you, and be as quick as you can. Hannah can stay and help me," her voice was urgent and anxious.

"And show him where to come," she called after us as we went.

It was almost dark by the time we reached the doctor's door. When at last he answered our urgent knocking, we breathed a sigh of relief.

"Doctor, you're to come quick, it's the hat.... the stranger... he's very bad, can hardly breathe," John blurted out breathlessly as the astonished doctor looked at us with a confused expression on his face.

"Would you mind repeating that again, slowly," he said.

"It's the stranger who lives in the far glen.

We found him lying outside, and he's very sick,'' Sara said taking over.

"We will show you where to go,'' John butted in again.

The doctor let out a long low sigh, before he spoke. "And I had hoped for a quiet night. Wait until I get my coat.''

We climbed into the old black Ford, and headed for the far glen guiding the good doctor on his way. The laneway narrowed, and the car had to slow to a crawl as it bumped its way over the rough surface.

"Where in hell does this man live?'' I've been on some rough roads in my time, but this takes the biscuit.''

The car bumped to an abrupt halt as the lane suddenly ran out. "Now what?'' he barked from the darkness.

"We have to walk it, the rest of the way,'' John ventured in a small voice from the back seat.

"Come on then lead the way. Nobody in their right state of mind should ever become a country doctor,'' he grumbled from behind as he followed us across the soggy rough terrain that led to the sick stranger's abode. We heard a splash, followed by a string of curses, as his foot went into a watery hole.

At last we reached the patient's house much to the doctor's relief.

"You stay here until I come out, for I will never find my way out of this damned hole on my own," he ordered before going in.

We peered through the window as the doctor examined him, first the stethoscope was moved from back to front, shaking his head at Mary to indicate how serious his condition was.

Then we turned our heads away when he produced a giant syringe with needle attached. "Poor hat," John said with a shudder.

When at last he emerged from the house accompanied by Mary, we heard him say. "Pneumonia, the lungs are full of fluid.

Just give him plenty of fluids, and keep him propped up. But, I wouldn't hold out too much hope."

"Thank you anyway doctor."

While John and Micheal escorted him back through the darkness, Mary said. "I want you two to stay with me tonight. I couldn't stay here on my own... please..." she added pleading.

And so began the long night vigil with the sick stranger. We brought in the firewood he had stacked neatly at the gable of the cottage. The wood smelt of the sea, and spat and spluttered as it burned from the salt.

"No turf here, he must have spent his days collecting driftwood," Mary commented as she made up the fire.

As we looked around the cottage we noted how neat and clean it all was. By the oil light we examined all the strange objects sitting on shelves around the room, strange carved statues with grotesque gargoyle like faces. The air was scented with strange spices that were alien to our nostrils.

"Not a holy picture in sight," Hannah said with a shudder.

"He must be a heathen," I added with conviction.

Throughout the long night the stranger remained semiconscious, and at times he muttered in a strange foreign language as his fever mounted. He looked a pitiful sight as he hovered between life and death. His old felt hat hung sorrowfully on the bedpost, it was the first time we had ever seen him without it on his head.

In the wee hours he began to cough, as rasping choking sounds came from his throat. Courage deserted us, and we headed outside into the darkness fearing the end was near.

Into the black cold night air we mouthed silent prayers for the stranger... heathen or not.

A few minutes later we peered fearfully through the window, and saw that he was still alive. He was propped up higher on the pillows with his eyes open.

Two days later we found the stranger well enough to sit up in a chair by the fire, the felt hat back on his head.

"You look a lot better," Hannah said when we went in.

"I have been playing hide and seek with undertakers all my life, and it seems he won't get a penny from me for a while yet," he said with a lopsided grin. "It seems I have a lot to thank you for." His blue piercing eyes scanned our faces for what seemed like an eternity before he spoke again.

"If you had asked me a few weeks back if this old life was worth living, I would have answered no, but I was wrong."

We waited for him to explain further, but he said no more.

As we were about to leave, he removed the felt hat, then from the lining he produced four ten shilling notes, and in spite of our protests he handed one to each of us.

"Never look a gift horse in the mouth, and anyway you earned it. Come back soon," he said as we reached the door.

During the following months 'the stranger' became no longer strange to us. He told us about all the far away places where he had lived, Africa, India, The Far East, places that had only been names in geography books became real and alive.

The strange looking statues and ornaments each had a story to tell about strange far away places and cultures.

One stormy winter's night we went to the far glen as usual, he was seated in his usual chair looking at the contents in a folder. He hastily tried to put the contents back when he saw us, but a photograph fell to the ground. Hannah bent to pick it up. It was a photograph of a young woman and a small child. An awkward silence followed before he spoke.

"That is...was, my wife and daughter."

"Are they dead or what?"

"No she ran off with someone who I thought was my friend. Since that time I vowed to trust no man," his eyes held a look of despair mixed with anger as they stared at the ceiling.

"Are you a heathen because of that?" John suddenly asked.

"Who says I'm a heathen?" He made no reply, instead he nodded in my direction. I could feel the blood rush to my face, 'I'll kill you when I get you outside' I vowed, overcome with angry humiliation. Then we heard his laughter fill the awkward silence. "Well, well, you can always rely on children for honesty," he chuckled. Then he cleared his throat before he spoke again.

"I don't think I'm a heathen. A heathen is someone who doesn't recognise the God of Christianity or any other religion. Well, I do believe in a creator, therefore I can't be a heathen. Does that answer your question?" We nodded silently, and I breathed a sigh of relief.

Several years had came and went since the stranger left the far glen, until the small parcel arrived in the post, addressed to John. It contained no letter or note of explanation; just the old felt hat. He gazed at it for a while, and then put it on his head, as all eyes looked on with question marks.

"The last time I saw him, I asked him if he would leave me his hat when he died...and he did."

# A School Day Remembered

A great surge of excitement filled me on that stormy December day. We were due to break up for the Christmas holidays on this day, and the thought of trudging home through the snow added to the glee.

The snow mounted against the school windows as the wind gusted and howled around the drafty school house.

The silence of the schoolroom was only broken by the wind and an occasional snore from the schoolmaster slumped on his chair behind the desk, with his back to the turf fire.

The schoolmaster was usually, if not actually drunk.

On his bad days he would fall into a heavy doze, from which the noise of his snores or the din of his neglected class usually woke him up.

Today, the class was unusually quiet, when someone in the front desk dropped a wooden pencil case, The clatter woke him up.

He started up wildly, perhaps imagining from

the noise that he was under enemy fire. He seized the wooden backed duster and flung it towards the blackboard, we all ducked automatically to avoid any serious injury. He then proceeded to tell us what a useless bunch we were, and how unfortunate he was to have to contend with such a class. It all fell on deaf ears as we had heard it many times before.

His eyes wandered to the pupils on the front desk. His gaze lingered on the small girl who had dropped the pencil case. She had obviously dipped her pen in the ink well once too often, her hands and work-book were badly ink stained. He ordered her out to wash her hands, scolding as she went about the untidy and ink stained copy book. He must have found it amusing, his face softened momentarily, but soon hardened again into its accustomed lines of discontent and ill-humour.

He suddenly noticed the snow piled against the windows, and swiftly walked over to look out. We waited with baited breath, would this mean he would let us go home early? Yes, we read him like a book. "Home," he shouted.

We packed our few belongings into our school bags and filed out into the snow, leaving behind the sound of Charlie muttering about how glad he was to be rid of us for a couple of weeks.

The snow drifted on a strong north east wind and despite our chilblains and frozen extremities, everyone was in a jolly holiday mood, all that is, except for Charlie, the school master. We trudged on with heads bent, it was too cold for much talk between us.

In the distance through the veil of snow we saw a horse and cart approaching in the opposite direction. As the horse drew closer the man on the cart jumped down, and going to the horse's head he turned him around.

"Jump in," he shouted.

It was Robert. We all piled into the cart, and were each given a bag to cover our legs. Now our cup overflowed. If it had been a golden coach with six prancing steeds instead of old Nelly and the cart we couldn't have been happier.

Old Nelly plodded on her head bent against the biting wind as we all sang in the back of the cart, chatting about how we were going to resurrect last year's broken wrecks of sleighs. We also decided to include in our bed-time prayers a special request for a good sharp frost.

Slowly, but surely we arrived home safely in the gathering gloom. Nelly stopped to deposit each small passenger safely at their door.

The memory of the warmth of the kitchen and hot soup remain part of my happy childhood memories to this day.

Charlie the schoolmaster, Robert my father and many others have long since gone to meet their maker.

Lingering memories of that day are still fresh in my memory.

# To Raise The Dead

We dawdled along the lane as usual on our way home from school.

"Only two weeks to go to the Christmas holidays," Joe said holding his hands in prayer like fashion close to his face.

"It's time we started rehearsals for the Christmas rhyming," Sara piped up. At that we all sat down on the ditch to make our plans. After much deliberation and a few arguments, it was decided that rehearsals would commence in our barn on Saturday night.

Saturday night came, and still the disagreements went on. The trouble was everyone wanted to be 'Jimmy funny, who collected the money.' At last an agreement was reached; John had secured the much prized role of Jimmy.

We practiced our individual rhymes, until we learned them off by heart.

Eventually we were rehearsed enough to set off on our first engagement. Clad in old borrowed clothing, at least five sizes too big, and with our individual plastic face masks in place, we set off on our first call through the darkness. As the dwellings were some considerable distance apart, we had to trudge along through dark lane-ways, and up and down steep braes to reach our audience.

Soon we arrived at Mc Laughlins; our first assignment. Taking a deep breath we knocked at the door. When it was opened, we asked in unison, "Any admission for the Christmas rhymers?" The door was opened wider and we were granted admission, as was the tradition. We went in, two at a time, and said our part of the ritual. When that part was completed we sang our songs, accompanied by Joe on the mouth organ.

That part finished, John made his entrance as Jimmy funny.

He ran around the floor, shaking his coin tin, and chanting.

HERE I COME WEE JIMMY FUNNY,
I'M THE MAN THAT LIFTS THE MONEY,
ALL SILVER, NO BRASS, BAD
HALFPENNYS WON'T PASS,
IT'S MONEY I WANT, IT'S MONEY I
CRAVE,
IF YOU DON'T GIVE ME MONEY,
I'LL CURSE YOU TO THE GRAVE.

114

With the money safely in the tin, the family members dutifully applauded us, and we took our leave.

And so on, and on, we trudged from house to house until our legs were tired, at which point we called it a night.

With only a few more houses which had not had the pleasure of our show, we set out on the last night, with only four more days until Christmas.

We stood at the bottom of Johnnie Malonie's laneway debating about whether or not it was worth the climb.

"It's a long walk up that hill, and it might not be worth it." Joe said.

"Oh, go on it's the last call, we might as well." I coaxed.

About half way up the steep hill, the torch light picked up a shiny object poking out of the hedge. On closer investigation we saw it was a bike. When we shone the torch a little further, we saw two hob nail boots, with legs attached to them.

"Oh, my good God, it's Johnnie. He must be dead," Joe said , with fear in his voice.

I shook him gently, and called, "Johnnie, Johnnie, wake up." But there was no response, as seven terror stricken small faces stared down at the motionless figure in disbelief. "What if they think we killed him. What will we do?" Sara asked.

"Don't be stupid, how could anybody think we killed him. My father will know what to do, I'll run and get him," I said.

"You all stay here, I'll be back as quick as I can."

Tucking my mother's old coat into the rope belt, I took off at speed in the direction of home.

Bursting breathlessly through the door, I stammered "Daddy, Daddy, Johnnie Mc... he's dead... lying in the hedge,"

I watched my father casually put on his boots, and light the hurricane lamp, with mounting impatience. 'Why isn't he hurrying with such a crisis in progress,' I thought. Unable to stand it any longer I said. "Please, please for heaven's sake hurry. He's dead."

"He may not be as dead as you think," he said as we set off.

"That's stupid. How many ways is there to die?"

"Only the one, only the one way," he said with amusement in his voice, that only served to anger me all the more.
Eventually we reached the spot in the hedge. Everyone stood back while my father took a look at the dead man.

Giving him a couple of hard shakes he bellowed.

"Come on Johnnie, get up out of that. It's too cold a night to sleep there."

Then we heard a grunt, to our great relief. We watched in stunned silence, while my father helped him out of the hedge.

Then he lifted his bicycle up for him, and off he went, wheeling it on up the hill.

"It's just like Lazarus rising from the dead," a small voice spoke from behind.

"Not quite," I don't think Lazarus would have had such a strong smell of whiskey about him somehow."

# Beginnings

When years seem to disappear
Like leaves in an Autumn gale,
And in the dark days
When layers of cloud-
Obscure and drain all colour
from the landscape.
Nothing can take away,
Memory of a perfect day
And a bright beginning.

# A Winter Tale
# And A Summer Ghost

We walked up the steep hill and along a narrow
lane to reach Jimmy's house. The house was
tucked neatly under a hill, and was sheltered by
six pine trees.

He was seated by a roaring fire made up of
turf and bog fir; one end of which streached a
considerable length down the floor.

"Welcome to you all. It's a raw cold night,"
he greeted us, pushing the bog fir a bit furthur
into the fire.

"Try as I might I couldn't get this fir block
split up, and in the finish, I broke the shaft of
my hatchet," he said sitting down again. The
dancing flames leaped and danced around the
big log of fir, lighting up the weather beaten
creases in his face, and deep set blue eyes
framed by dark bushy eyebrows.

Jimmy was the best storyteller in the
neighbourhood, and we were regular visitors.
We loved to listen to his stories about ghosts

and banshees.

"I'm just about to make my cocoa, would you all like a cup?"

"Aye, thanks," we all chanted.

With our cups of hot cocoa in our hands we were ready for a good frightening ghost story.

"Have you any new ghost stories to tell us?" Joe asked.

"Well now, let me see if I can think of any I haven't told you before. Mmm....mmm," he muttered, staring into the fire in deep concentration. Then he lit his pipe, lifting his eyebrows with a frown to keep them safe from the flames that leapt from the thin fold of newspaper that he used instead of matches.

As the story progressed we could feel the goose pimples rising on the backs of our necks. His bright blue eyes moved from one wide eyed scared face to the other as he told the story.

"I had just reached the top of the brae beside O'Neill's derelict house, when I saw the black cloaked figure of a woman walk right through the stone ditch, not an inch from me. As I stood there in the moonlight I knew that I had witnessed a being, not of this world."

Walking home through the darkness we linked arms for safety, and when we reached O'Neill's brae we shuffled along in a huddled fearfull mass, with eyes and ears on red alert for the cloaked figure of a supernatural woman; but she was nowhere to be seen.

"My father says there is no such things as ghosts. He says Jimmy just makes up his stories as he goes along," Sara said in a shaky wee voice, as her shaking fingertips dug into my upper arm.

"Well I believe in ghosts no matter what your father says. And besides a world without ghosts would be no fun," Joe's voice came back from the blackness. Much to our disappointment we reached home without a ghost or ghoul to be seen.

In the early spring a builder from the nearby town started to renovate O'Neill's old house. Rotting windows and doors were replaced, the roof was repaired, and finally the walls were whitewashed.

One day in late June as we made our way to the shore, we saw that the house was occupied.

"Holiday makers from Scotland have rented the place out," Pat informed us while we stood in the door of the byre as he milked the cows.

"It must be thirty years or more since anybody slept under that roof," he added as he headed for the house carrying two buckets of milk.

July began wet and windy, but soon gave way

to warm sunshine. One morning on our way to
the shore two young girls with red hair sat on
the stone ditch outside O'Neill's.

"We are going down to the shore for a dip.
Do you want to come with us?" I asked them a
little shyly.

"I'll go and ask my Ma," the bigger of the
girls said as she hurried off into the house.

"What's your name?" Sara asked the girl
sitting on the wall.

"I'm Edith, and she's Fiona," she answered
nodding in the direction of her sister who had
just reappeared.

Before the day was out we had formed a
bond of friendship. They came from Glasgow,
and lived next door to the man who owned
O'Neill's old house.

The following morning we set off with our
new found friends on a tour of the
neighbourhood. As we rounded a corner in the
lane Johnny Mc Laughlin was putting his cows
out. Fiona stood in the middle of the lane and
let out a piercing yell, while the astonished
cows turned around and bolted back towards
the farmyard.

"God in heaven what possessed you to roar
like that?" Johnny spat throwing his stick to
the ground in anger.

From the ditch sandwiched between two
hawthorn bushes Edith said in her Glasgow lilt,

"She is terrified of cows, and so am I."

"If I'm any judge, the cows were more terrified of you wailing like a banshee than you were of them. But you are city wains I suppose," he added graciously.

To our amusement their fear of animals extended to anything on four legs, and that included Neddy. However, a ride in the cart was irresistible, and facing backwards they giggled with glee as they bumped noisily along the lane. But when Neddy in one of his stubborn moods sat down between the shafts of the cart, they hightailed it to a safe distance, while we tried in vain to persuade him to get up again.

On the last day of July we all sat on the beach reluctant to say goodbye to our Glasgow friends.

"I wish we could stay longer, but we will come back next summer." Fiona said a little sadly.

"We all want to come back next year except my mother," Edith said, as she absently made holes in the sand with a stick.

"Why does your mother not want to come back?" Sara asked.

"Because she thought she saw the ghost of a woman in a black clock at the head of the stairs."

# The Oak Tree

Old noble oak still standing firm
In the empty silent school yard.
Still spreading your branches-
Like mother arms that once enfolded us,
Sheltering us from sun and rain,
And from high in your branches
hidden from sight-
Among your lush leaves-
We could daydream as we watched-
the mountain streams tumbling over rocks-
To join the river that run in and out-
to the shimmering sea.

You silenty heard our childhood secrets,
You have the wisdom that only time brings,
And in your roots you carry the knowledge-
From which all new springs can grow.

# The Fox And The Funeral

The ground was hard underfoot when we set off for school on a cold November morning. A hare sat in a nearby field, his head moving warily from right to left, before sprinting across the frozen grass.

Pat stood at the cross-roads with a serious expression on his face, his breath coming like bursts of steam in the frosty air.

"Cold morning," he greeted us absently his eyes scanning the sorrounding fields. "A fox took one of Martha's geese last night. I'll get him yet, even if I have to sit up all night. I'll get him," he repeated nodding as if to reassure himself.

The sound of the school bell mingled with the excited calls of the children at play, reluctantly we shuffled towards the teacher and the clanging bell. Each young face had a bewildered look, it was just fifteen minutes into lunch break.

"Mrs. Mc Colgans funeral will pass here in a few minutes," the teacher said. "I want you all to stand quietly and respectfully until the entire funeral has passed. And remember, I'll be watching every one of you," he added, scanning each upturned face sternly by way of warning.

We watched the hearse as it slowly made its way towards us, the black horse moving at an even pace, his head bowed forward. Mourners walked slowly behind, their feet crunching through the frosted Autumn leaves. Two black motor cars followed at the rear, we could see fleeting glimpses of the black clad white faces of the next of kin as they slowly passed. Gradually we dispersed from our positions, at first in silence and then voices raised as play resumed.

Sara and I walked over to the oak tree and sat down underneath on the fallen leaves.

"It's horrible to die and be put in a hole in the ground," Sara said staring straight ahead, the light breeze blowing her auburn curls." But it's only the body that goes into the ground I suppose," she added.

"It's such a pity we couldn't do it without dying," I reasoned.

"Do what without dying?"

"Go to heaven."

"You say the most stupid things sometimes," she replied as a smile slowly crossed her face.

The sharp clang of the bell heralding the end of playtime also ended our conversation about death.

In the classroom Miss Doherty got the afternoon lessons into progress. "I want second and third class to write an essay," she began. "As you probably know already the fox has been raiding the local hen-houses. So, let me see how much you all know about the crafty fox?" she concluded, as we settled down to write our essays.

The particular fox I had in mind was clever enough to know that there was a funeral, and with this knowledge was able to choose the heaven sent opportunity to raid the hen-house of the deceased. I had just started to write when the pain started in my lower jaw. "What's wrong?" Sara whispered.

"I've got toothache," I whispered back with one hand holding my aching jaw. Instantly her hand shot into the air.

"Miss Doherty, Mary has toothache."

"Come over here to the window and let me have a look," she said. "Now open wide and show me which one. Mmm... mmm... I can see the one that's causing the trouble. Fortunately it's a milk tooth, and it's loose." Going over to a drawer in her desk she came back with a spool of thread. I could feel her nimble fingers wiggle the tooth from side to side.

"Oh, look at the big ship," she suddenly exclaimed. While my eyes scanned the sea in vain, I felt the tug, and there was the tooth in between her finger and thumb. Sitting back in my seat.with the pain gone; in that instance of blessed relief I thought that Miss Doherty had suddenly sprouted a halo.

When we had handed in our essays, and as she read we watched as broad smiles periodically crossed her face. "Well, we must surely have the most clever and cunning foxes in the world if these tales you have penned are anything to go by," she said, still grinning. "It's difficult to choose the best one. But I think the winner is the fox Michael encountered. This particular fox made his den under a steep cliff. When he needed to get into his den in a hurry one wild winter's night, with two snarling dogs at his heels, and an angry farmer following behind with a pitch fork. The farmer watched from the edge of the cliff in astonishment, as the wild old fox swung on a hawthorn bush and reached his den, while the poor dogs fell to their deaths over the steep cliff."

# The Doctor Knows Best

The youth of the neighbourhood stood in a group at the corner on that Autumn afternoon of the big wind.

The fury of the wind had gone, leaving an eery silent stillness in it's wake.

Michael Mac Connell's hay stack was missing, it's remains could be seen entangled in the fuchsia and hawthorn hedges, like giant spiders' webs.

Johnny sauntered into sight down the brae.

"Where you off to?" someone asked.

"To give Mick a hand to fix a roof in the village."

All hands abandoned the corner and followed him, commenting on the storm damage as they went.

Mick Mallon's black van sat motionless, when we rounded the bend. We watched him turn the cranking handle furiously, as he tried in vain to start the engine.

"To hell with it anyway, not even a kick in it," he spat rubbing his shoulder. "I don't know a damn how I'm going to get the ladder and slates down to Murphy's roof," he muttered angrily giving the van a kick.

"We could take them down in the donkey's cart," John piped up.

He let out a long low sigh before he answered.

"I suppose I will have to take you up on your offer. The slates are to heavy to carry, and this confounded yoke won't budge," he gave it another kick for good measure as he walked off.

He stopped at the door, and called back,

"Be as quick as you can. And you go with him Johnny, I have to get that roof fixed before dark."

The loud rattle of the iron wheels on the rocky lane could be heard in the still air, long before the cart came into view. When the slates were loaded and the ladder balanced on the cart, all hands set off at a steady, noisy rattle for Murphy's roof; all except Mick.

"I'll follow you up in a wee while," he said lamely. "Take it easy with the slates now, they break easy."

"Don't worry, Neddy is not in the habit of

breaking into a sudden gallop,'' John said reassuringly.

With the slates and ladder safely transported to Murphy's, everyone waited for Mick to arrive.

When he showed up, he spent the first half hour explaining to all who passed, how his trusted van had let him down badly, and how he was reduced to such a low form of transport.

The gaping hole in the roof soon began to disappear when he got to work on it. Up and down the ladder he went laiden with slates; the noise of his hammering filling the air while Johnny held the ladder for each descent.

A football rolled into Johnny's path, he left the ladder only momentarily to kick the ball back in the direction it came from when it happened. The ladder slipped just as Mick was making his descent; it crashed to the ground with a loud bang, and Mick lay in a motionless heap. Johnny stared at the lifeless figure open mouthed, he looked like an animal in long grass scenting smoke in the wind.

"Oh God! oh God!" he repeated. "I was warned not to leave the ladder."

Mrs. Murphy bent over him in a state of anxiety, "Get the doctor, and be quick."

The doctor arrived in a very short time, and the onlookers stood aside to give him space. He was new to the area young, keen, and efficient they said. He glanced at the patient and then at the height from which he had fallen. With an apprehensive shake of the head he said, "It doesn't look good, I think he's dead."

Then from the figure on the ground came first a low moan, and then he spoke, "I'm not dead," he groaned.

Suddenly finding his voice, Johnny piped up,

"Oh, will you shut up, do you think you know better than the doctor."

# Acknowledgments

Brian Bonner

Sean Beattie

Robert Welch

Brigid O'Donnell

Jan Mc Guinness

The Macklin Committee

To all my friends who have given me help
and support when I most needed it.

I must add my thanks to my husband Charles
for his loving support and good humour.